WP405
Intermediate
BOOK 5

Jane Smisor Bastien · Lisa Bastien · Lori Bastien

BASTIENS'
COLLAGE
OF SOLOS

D1621799

Bastiens' Collage of Solos, Book 5, is designed to captivate the interest and imagination of intermediate students with the three distinctive styles of Jane, Lisa, and Lori Bastien. These solos will add excitement to the repertoire for intermediate students of all ages!

Contents

*To reinforce the feeling of achievement, the teacher or student may put a ✓ when the page has been mastered.

ISBN 0-8497-9638-5

©1996 Neil A. Kjos Music Company, 4380 Jutland Drive, San Diego, California 92117
International copyright secured. All rights reserved. Printed in U.S.A.

Memories of Monte Carlo

Jane Smisor Bastien

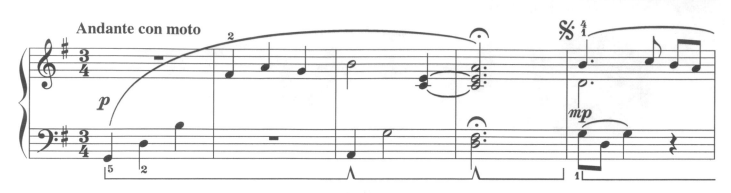

Mardi Gras Parade

Lisa Bastien

Boogie Time

Jane Smisor Bastien

Allegro con spirito

Indian Summer

Lisa Bastien

Sunflower Rag

Lori Bastien

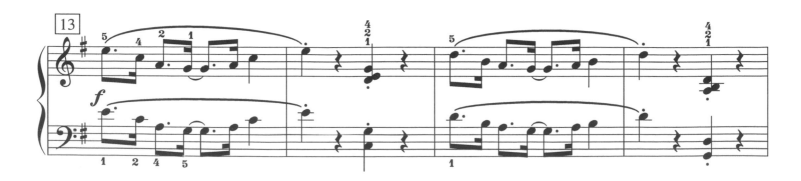

Capriccioso

Lori Bastien

Masquerade Ball

Lisa Bastien

Jazzy Fingers

Jane Smisor Bastien

Prelude at Sunset

Jane Smisor Bastien

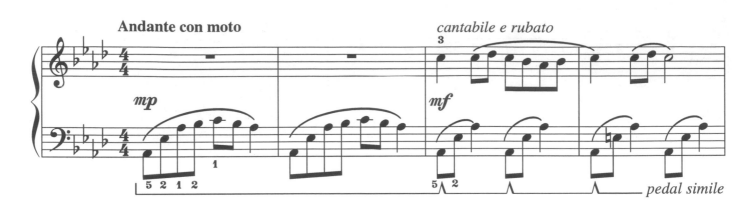

Evening Arabesque

Lori Bastien

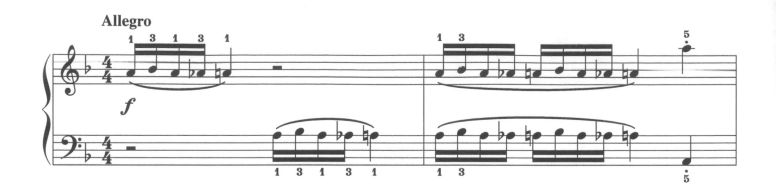

2nd time to Coda

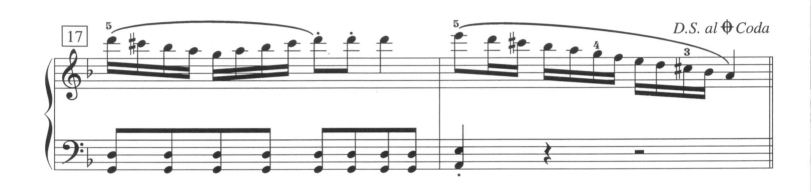